THE FIRST NOWELL

A NATIVITY PLAY

for soloists, S.A.T.B. chorus, and
small orchestra

Libretto adapted from Medieval Pageants by
SIMONA PAKENHAM

Music composed and arranged from traditional tunes by
R. VAUGHAN WILLIAMS
with additions by ROY DOUGLAS

OXFORD UNIVERSITY PRESS
MUSIC DEPARTMENT
WALTON STREET · OXFORD · OX2 6DP

NOTES

The work is scored for 2 flutes, oboe, 2 clarinets, bassoon, 2 horns, 2 trumpets, tenor trombone, bass trombone, timpani, harp and strings.

Full scores, vocal scores, and orchestral parts are on hire.

An arrangement of the accompaniment for strings and organ (or piano) is also available on hire.

Notes on production are provided in the libretto, which is on sale.

Details of how the work may be performed in a *concert version* are provided in this score.

CONCERT VERSION. The following numbers should be included:

1. Baritone Solo and Chorus	9. Chorus SSA
3. Soprano Solo	15. Baritone Solo and Chorus
4. Chorus	16. Chorus TTB
6. Chorus	17. Chorus
7. Soprano Solo	18. Orchestra only
8. Baritone Solo (or soprano chorus) and chorus	20. Soprano and Baritone Soli and Chorus

2, 5, and 12 may also be included if desired.

DURATION
STAGE VERSION: 50 minutes
CONCERT VERSION: 30 minutes

This work was first performed with the St. Martin-in-the-Fields Concert Orchestra and Singers conducted by John Churchill, and produced by Noel Iliff and Geraldine Stephenson, as part of the St. Martin-in-the-Fields Christmas Matinée held at the Theatre Royal, Drury Lane, on 19th December, 1958.

The purchase or hire of this work does not convey the right to perform, permission for which must be obtained from the publishers for stage performances, and from the Performing Right Society for performances of the concert version.

CHARACTERS

Speaking parts:—

CREATOR	ELIZABETH	CASPAR
GABRIEL	JOSEPH	MELCHIOR
MARY		BALTHAZAR

Speaking and singing parts:—

FIRST SHEPHERD (Baritone or Bass)

SECOND SHEPHERD (Tenor)

THIRD SHEPHERD (Tenor or Treble)

> The three shepherds need not be solo singers, for
> their acting is more important than their singing.

Singing parts:—

SOPRANO SOLOIST

BARITONE SOLOIST

ANGELS (Chorus: S.A.T.B.)

Silent parts:—

MARY'S TWO MAIDS

ATTENDANTS ON CASPAR, MELCHIOR AND BALTHAZAR

OTHER SHEPHERDS (Dancers)

THE FIRST NOWELL

MUSIC 1

PRELUDE (Baritone Solo and Chorus)

★ In the stage version, if the Chorus are behind the curtain, it may be
necessary for this section to be played by the orchestra only, until [J].

† The words in italics may be sung here if preferred

The First Nowell

The First Nowell

5

Melody and words of *The Truth from Above* from *The Oxford Book of Carols* by permission

The First Nowell

6

And we were heirs to end-less woes, Till God the Lord did in - ter - pose; And so a — pro - mise soon did run That he would re - deem — us — by — his son. —

Hns.

Hns.

p (pizz.) (Wind with Chorus)

Vlns, Violas and Cellos.

The First Nowell

The First Nowell

Warning cue: For that he beguiléd was.....

Cue: **Creator:** I would that my son should manhood take

OMIT IN CONCERT VERSION

MUSIC 2

(Orchestra only)

Creator *(spoken)* My son shall in a maiden light, Against the fiend of hell to fight; God and man

both shall he be, And she both mother and maiden free.

Creator: And I will that all prophecy....

Warning cue: Her have I chosen, that maiden sweet......

Cue: **Creator:** Prepare thee, Gabriel, and wend

OMIT IN CONCERT VERSION

MUSIC 2a

Repeat MUSIC 2 from [S]
then segue MUSIC 3

MUSIC 3
(Soprano Solo)

The First Nowell

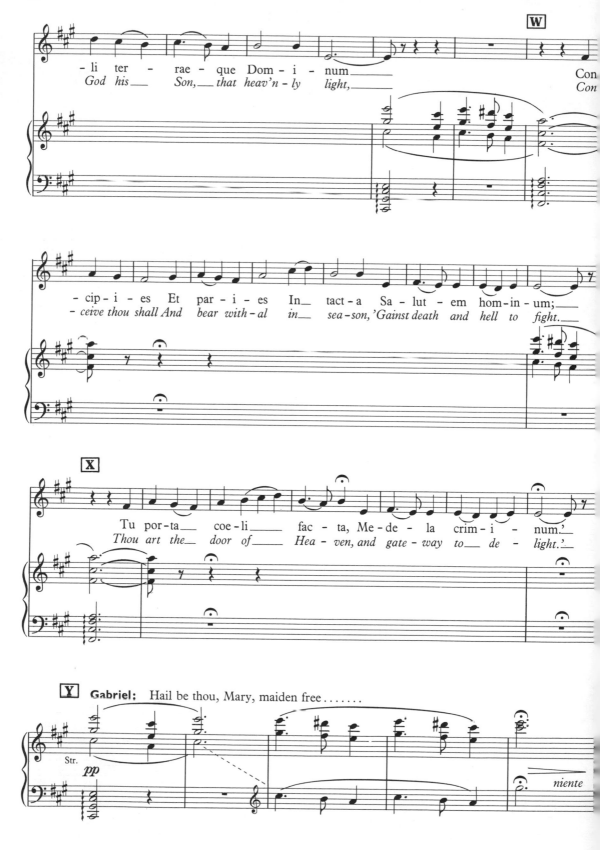

Warning cue: Now since that God wills this to be.....

Cue: **Mary:** This word that thou hast said

MUSIC 4
(Chorus)

[Completed by R.D.]

Melody and words of *The Salutation Carol* from *The Oxford Book of Carols* by permission

The First Nowell

12

The First Nowell

Warning cue: Elizabeth, for this will we. . . .
Cue: **Mary:** And laud to his liking

OMIT IN CONCERT VERSION

MUSIC 5
(Soprano Solo)

The First Nowell

14

*Finish here if preferred.

The First Nowell

15

Warning cue: Elizabeth, cousin, let us do this . . . . . .

Cue: **Mary:** Will witness of my deed

MUSIC 6
(Chorus)

The First Nowell   Melody and words of *The Cherry Tree Carol* from *The Oxford Book of Carols* by permission

16

The First Nowell

5. Then bow - ed down the high-est tree Un - to the Vir-gin's hand. Then.
eat your cher-ries, Ma - ry, O eat your cher-ries now, O__

she cried 'See,__ Jo - seph, I have cher - ries at com-mand'. 6. 'O
eat your cher-ries, Ma - ry, That grow up - on the bough'.

Elizabeth: Good cousin Joseph,
God save thee . . . . .

Warning cue: These woes make me so heavy . . . . . .

Cue: **Joseph** For her misdeeds this day.

MUSIC 7
(Soprano Solo)

Andante tranquillo   [slightly revised by R. D.]

Soprano Solo

As Jo-seph was a - walk - ing, He__
*neith-er shall be__ cloth - èd In__

Str.

Viola Solo

*The second verse is to be sung in the Concert Version, but in the Stage Version it must be played by the orchestra only

The First Nowell   † In the orchestra the tune is omitted 1st time

heard an an - gel sing: 'This night there shall be born on earth our
pur - ple nor in pall, But all in fair lin - en As

2nd time **Gabriel** *(Spoken)*: Joseph, leave thy feeble thought! Take Mary, thy wife, and
dread thee naught, For wickedly she hath not wrought, But this is

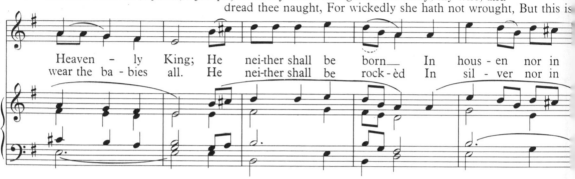

Heaven - ly King; He nei-ther shall be born In hous - en nor in
wear the ba - bies all. He nei-ther shall be rock - èd In sil - ver nor in

God his will. The child that she shall bear, I wis Of the Holy Ghost begotten is,
To save mankind that did amiss, And prophecy to fulfil

hall, Nor in the place of Par - a - dise, But in an ox' - s stall'.
gold, But in a wood - en cra - dle That rocks up - on the mould'.

'He

Viola Solo

Oboe or
Fl.

Joseph: Ah! now I wot, if this is so . . . . . .

The First Nowell

Warning cue: Now Christ is come into our fold . . . . . .

Cue: **Joseph:** And with zeal I worship thee.

MUSIC 8

(Soprano or Baritone Solo, Chorus)

IN THE CONCERT VERSION THIS SHOULD BE SUNG BY THE BARITONE SOLOIST, OR BY ALL THE CHORUS SOPRANOS

The First Nowell

20

The First Nowell

21

The First Nowell

Gabriel *(spoken):* Arise up, Joseph, go home again To Mary, thy wife, tha[t]

is so free. To comfort her look that thou be fain, For a chaste maiden is she.

Joseph: Great Lord

my heart is no more sad, And of these tidings I am so glad That all my care away is cast; Therefore

Repeat only if necessary
NO REPEAT IN CONCERT VERSION

to Mary I will in haste.

Joseph: Mary, Mary, . . .

The First Nowell   † No change of tempo in Concert Version

Warning cue: Nay, dearest husband, dread thou nothing....

Cue: **Joseph:** Go we together in God's holy name.

MUSIC 9
(Women's Chorus)

Melody and words of *In Bethlehem City* by permission of J. B. Cramer & Co. Ltd.

The First Nowell

24

The First Nowell

The First Nowell

26

The First Nowell

The First Nowell

28

OMIT IN CONCERT VERSION

(Finish at **K** or **L** if necessary. [R.D.])

1st Shepherd: Lord, what these
weathers are cold......

Warning cue: For I trow, pardie ......

Cue: **1st Shepherd:** Ere it be noon

OMIT IN CONCERT VERSION

MUSIC 10

(Finish at **M** or **N** if necessary. [R.D.])

2nd Shepherd: Benedicite and Dominus ......

Warning cue: Now in dry, now in wet ......

Cue: **1st Shepherd:** Heard I him blow.

OMIT IN CONCERT VERSION

MUSIC 11

1st Shepherd: He comes here
at hand ......

Melody of *It's a Rosebud in June* (collected Cecil Sharp) by permission of Novello & Co. Ltd.

The First Nowell

Warning cue: Yet I would, ere we go, one gave us a song . . . . . .

Cue: **1st Shepherd:** Let see how ye chant.

OMIT IN
CONCERT
VERSION

MUSIC 12

(Shepherds Soli: Tenor I [or Treble], Tenor II, Bass)

The First Nowell

31

* (These bars are cued in the Woodwind parts in case the **Shepherds** are unable to sing in harmony)

The First Nowell

32

1st Shepherd: Lord, what I am sore, in point for to burst!
In faith I may no more; therefore will I rest.

2nd Shepherd: To sleep anywhere methink that I list.

The First Nowell

3rd Shepherd: Now I pray you
Lie down on this green.
Do as I say you.

OMIT IN
CONCERT
VERSION

MUSIC 13
(Chorus off-stage)

(★Cut from A to B if necessary [R.D.])

The First Nowell

34

★★From John Taverner's "The Western Wynde" Mass; chosen by R.V.W. and edited by R.D. from "Tudor Church Music" (O.U.P.)

The First Nowell

The First Nowell

36

Gabriel: Rise gentle herdsmen, for now he is born That shall take

from the fiend that Adam had lorn; That warlock to conquer, this night he is born. God is made

The First Nowell

your friend, now at this morn, He behests. At Bethlehem go see There lies so free In a crib so poorly,

a De — — i pa — — — — — is
born, *un* — — *to* *us* *a* *Son_____* *is*

in glo — ri - a De — — — —
for *un* - *to* *us,* *Un* — — *to*

in glo — ri - a De - i pa - - tris,
for *un* - *to* *us,* *un* - *to* *us_____* *a*

- ri - a De - i pa — — — tris, pa — — —
- *to* *us* *a* *Child* *is_____* *born,_____* *a_____* *Son* *is*

R.H.

Betwixt two beasts [J]

- tris. A — — — — — — — men, A -
given.

- i pa — — tris. A — — men, A -
us *a* *Son_____* *is* *given.*

pa — — — — tris. A — — men, A — —
Son_____ *is* *given.*

- tris. A- — — — — — men, A - — —
given.

[J]

R.H. L.H.

The First Nowell

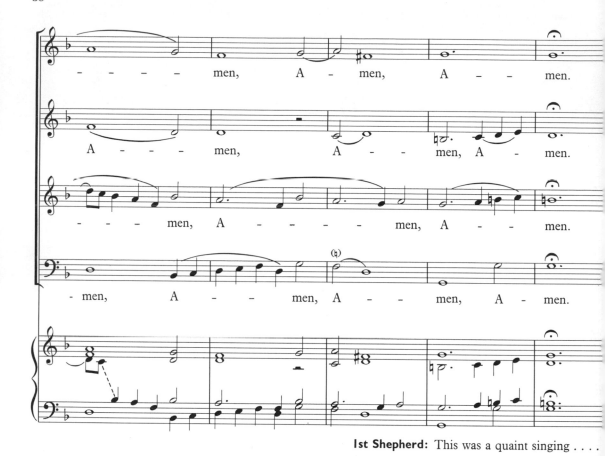

1st Shepherd: This was a quaint singing . . . .

Warning cue: He spake of a bairn . . . .

Cue: **3rd Shepherd:** Be merry and not sad—of mirth is our song!

OMIT IN
CONCERT
VERSION

MUSIC 14

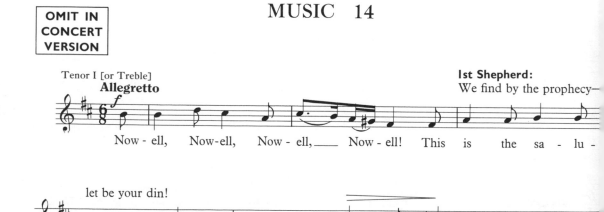

The First Nowell

Warning cue: But the angel said

Cue: **3rd Shepherd:** He was poorly arrayed,

MUSIC 15
(Baritone Solo* and Chorus)

[adapted by R.D.]

3rd Shep. **2nd Shep.**
Both meek and mild. Go we now, let us fare; the place is us near

*In the Stage version the first four bars may be sung by the **Shepherds** as they exit.

Melody and words of *On Christmas Night (The Sussex Carol)* reprinted by permission of Stainer and Bell Ltd.

The First Nowell

40

The First Nowell

1st Shepherd: Hail, comely and clean......

Warning cue: Farewell, lady, so fair to behold......
Cue: **1st Shepherd:** What grace we have found!

MUSIC 16
(Shepherds Soli: Tenor I [or Treble], Tenor II, Bass)

[added by R.D.]

2nd Shep.
Come forth; now we are won:

3rd Shep.
To sing we are bound.

IN CONCERT VERSION
CHORUS TENORS & BASSES

The First Nowell

42

Tenor I
[or Treble

The First Nowell

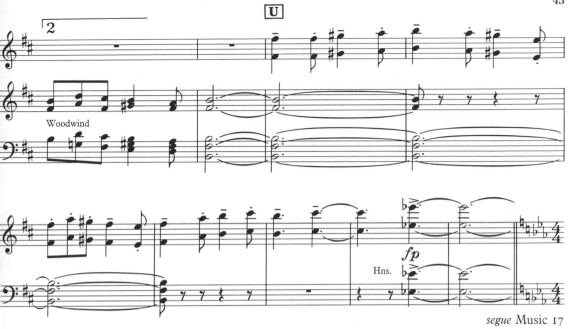

segue Music 17

MUSIC 17
(Chorus)

[Constructed from sketches, by R.D.]

*Chorus: Tenors and Basses in unison

Maestoso con moto ♩=132 (♩ =66)

[Translation by R.V.W.] *Verse 1* How bright-ly

shone the morn-ing star,——— Which led the

IN THE CONCERT VERSION THE CHORUS SING BOTH VERSES

In the stage version the chorus sing in the second verse
only, using the words of the first verse, as printed in italics.

The First Nowell

The First Nowell

The First Nowell

46

The First Nowell

The First Nowell

48

Caspar: The star over yonder stable is..

The First Nowell

Warning cue: A fair maiden, sirs....

Cue: **Balthazar:** Three persons are therein....

MUSIC 18
(Orchestra)

[added by R.D.]

FINISH HERE IN CONCERT VERSION
TO MUSIC 20

Caspar: Hail be thou....

[If necessary for stage purposes this number may end at ⊕ or †]

The First Nowell

50

Warning cue: That him today have honoured here....
Cue: **Mary:** That I dare undertake.

MUSIC 19
(Chorus)

OMIT IN CONCERT VERSION

[Constructed from sketches, by R.D.]

* In the Stage version it may be advisable for the Chorus to sing in
the first section only, *i.e.* Verse 2. A large optional cut is indicated

The First Nowell

51

The First Nowell

52

The First Nowell

The First Nowell

S.
A.
T.
B.
M
morn - ing star still shines to - day
let us all with one ac - cord
To
Give
(Chorus parts cued in Brass throughout)
N
guide men in the heaven - ly way,
prai - ses to the in - fant Lord
Where
With
1
shall be joy and sing - ing.
wor - ship and thanks - giv - ing.
So

The First Nowell

Finish at † if necessary

The First Nowell

56

Warning cue: You Kings, I say, with sure intent....
Cue: **Balthazar:** Farewell and have good day.

MUSIC 20
(Full)

[Completed by R.D.]

The First Nowell

The First Nowell

† Shepherds (in Stage Version) and Baritone Solo

(Chorus not cued)

Str. & W. Wind

Brass

Verse 3 And by the light of

Born is the King of Is-ra-el. And by the light of that same

Born is the King of Is-ra-el. And by the light of

† In the stage Version it may be preferable for the **Shepherds** not to sing until Verse 4

that same star, Three Wise Men came from coun-try far; To seek for a

star, Three Wise Men came from coun-try far; To seek for a king was

that same star, Three Wise Men came from coun-try far; To seek for a

‡ At this point the original manuscript full score ends; the remainder of this section has been constructed and developed, by R.D., from the composer's fragmentary sketches.

The First Nowell

The First Nowell

The First Nowell

** See overleaf for alternative ending

Fine

The First Nowell

★★ Alternative ending [added by R.D.]

★★ This alternative ending may be necessary in the Stage version, if there is no curtain and the cast have to disperse in view of the audience. It may also be used in the Concert Version if preferred.　　[R.D.]